Fiction

writing frames

for infants

Steve Harrison   *COPIABLE*   Patricia Harrison

Acknowledgements

© 1999 Belair Publications, on behalf of the authors.
Apex Business Centre, Boscombe Road, Dunstable, LU5 4RL.
Email: belair@belair-publications.co.uk

Steve Harrison and Patricia Harrison hereby assert their moral rights to be identified as the authors of this work in accordance with the Copyright, Designs and Patents Act 1988.

Editor: Helen Banbury
Layout artist: Suzanne Ward
Illustrations: Catherine Ward, Simon Girling Associates
                 Kirsty Wilson, Graham-Cameron Illustration
Cover design: Ed Gallagher

First published in 1999 by Belair Publications.
Reprinted 2000 (twice)
Reprinted 2001
Reprinted 2002

British Library Cataloguing in Publication Data. A catalogue record for this publication is available from the British Library.

ISBN 1 84191 018-X

Introduction

Writing Frames have been shown to assist many children in the structuring of their writing. Children who lack confidence in their writing find such support extremely helpful. Many frames currently in use in schools are 'generic' frames, such as explanations, reports, investigations, comparisons, etc. These are included in these *Belair Writing Frames* but we have taken the concept of writing frames a step further. This new generation of writing frames is linked closely not only to the process of writing, but also to the content of the English curriculum which provides the context for much of the writing children will do in class.

Using the frames

A key purpose of writing frames is to develop high quality writing. Children should know they are expected to write in full sentences, punctuated appropriately, and in a legible manner. Many copiable sheets in the past have required single word responses. These frames require a broader range of responses, including coherent prose.

Writing Frames on CD

These *Belair Writing Frames* are the first frames to be produced for primary schools in two formats – on paper and on CD. The disks offer enormous opportunities for both teachers and children.

Key features

- The frames can be altered. If you, as a teacher, want to modify the number of boxes or the text starters in any frame, you can do so easily. This allows you to tailor the work more specifically to the needs of your class or to individuals within it. You could simplify text; add complexity to the language and structure; make cloze activities; or provide various options as answers, to be deleted to leave the correct answer.
- Paper-based frames are inflexible. They impose limits on how much children can write. The CDs have no such limits. The text will simply scroll on and the frame, in effect, expands to accommodate whatever the child wants to write.
- At 'print-out' stage the boxes simply disappear. The child prints out a page of continuous text. No-one can see what part was provided in advance and what part added by the child. However, those pages with pictures and tables retain the boxes and print out a 'screen shot' of all the elements on the screen.

- The CDs can allow pictures and diagrams to be inserted into the frames, ready for printing (see the Help file on the CD for instructions). The CDs also contain subject-specific vocabulary. Children who need a word can check the directory and paste that word into their text. You or the children can add words to this directory, as appropriate.
- Finally, you can of course modify frames on-screen and then print them out for children to use as paper frames.

Target pupils

The options available through the provision of CDs means that work can be tailored to the specific needs of individual pupils. Pupils with learning difficulties can have simplified frames, which provide strong support for their particular needs in developing literacy. Able and gifted children can be challenged to produce high quality, extended writing across the curriculum.

Contents and Teachers' Notes

Familiar Nursery Rhymes

- Having heard, read and recited familiar rhymes, children should use the frames to write the rhyme themselves.
- Teachers using the disks can choose to add or delete helpful words.
- Children should make judgements about different nursery rhymes, as well as recognising the patterns of repetition.
- Encourage children to think about the range of characters featured in rhymes; note, for example, how frequently the word 'little' is used and how animals, as well as people, often appear. Ask the children to compose their own nursery rhymes using such features.

Familiar Fairy Stories

These frames provide a variety of opportunities to focus on different aspects of familiar stories.

- The children should recount the main points of the story in chronological sequence and identify repetitive language.

- Focus on the patterned language used by Red Riding Hood to the Wolf in his disguise.
- Look at the chronological sequence and the repetitive language of both the Wolf and the Pigs.
- Children who can provide interesting alternative endings should be encouraged to write, tell and display them.

- Before this frame can be approached, the children will need to have heard and, preferably, read the four tales listed in the chart. The emphasis in discussion should be on the actions of 'good' and 'bad' characters.

- After using a range of story beginnings in the frame, the children should be given the opportunity to use such forms in their subsequent writing. Note, too, how certain beginnings can fix stories in the recent or distant past.

- The frame offers an opportunity to explore the elements of a traditional fairy tale structure, i.e.
  Once upon a time – the opening
  Sadly – the problem (conflict)
  Happily – the resolution
  Finally – the conclusion

- In writing this frame, the children must be aware of the different roles played by various characters, the notion of plot and the importance of a conclusion.

Counting Rhymes

- Both counting rhymes are traditional and, therefore, there is a recognised content which children may know.
- In addition to introducing the familiar rhyme, the teacher may wish to encourage the children to produce their own alternatives.
- Teachers using the disk can add to or delete from the helpful words list.

Action Rhymes

- Children should associate specific actions with each part of the rhyme. This assists in the recollection of key words and sequence.
- Predictable and repeated patterns occur throughout. Children should be encouraged to develop their own, using similar rhyming patterns.
- The first two action rhymes provide visual cues, to help the children identify a rhyming word. The latter two rhymes offer no cues other than the final rhyming word for each two lines.

Contents and Teachers' Notes

A World of Stories

- In order for children to appreciate stories and poems from a wide range of cultures, it is important for the teacher to identify the origin of stories as they are experienced by the class.
- The first three frames in this section ask the children to explain the features of particular stories that indicate their origins.
- Children will need to have heard and read a diverse range of stories.
- The character profile of Pinocchio can be presented as a poster but should include physical description, character outline and context of disappearance.
- This example of a Greek fable contains the classic feature of 'pride before a fall', followed, inevitably, by the moral of the story.

Aspects of Story

- The first four frames in this section can be used a number of times for character descriptions in a range of stories.

- This character profile is based solely on a written description.
- In addition to describing the behaviour in chronological sequence, the children will also make judgements about the behaviour and compare this character with others.
- This requires physical description without reference to personality or activity.
- The teacher can determine whether to have an 'open' category (any one at all) or a restricted list of who could be 'Wanted'.
- This provides a frame for patterned language with predictable developments. Teachers using the disk can substitute other characters and actions for those of the farmer.
- Share with the children a variety of 'tongue twisters' and 'riddles' before providing them with the frames to help them write their own.
- This frame is meant for fiction. A separate non-fiction resource is available.
- The children should compare books/poems by the same author and begin to recognise the patterns of setting, character, style, etc.

Mary Had a Little Lamb

Helpful Words

fleece
everywhere
snow

Mary _____

Its _____

And _____

_____

It _____

_____

That was _____

It made _____

_____

Name: _____ Date: _____

Fiction Writing Frames for Infants

Little Bo Peep

Helpful Words

sheep
doesn't
tails

Little _____

_____

And _____

_____

Leave _____

And _____

Wagging _____

Name: _____ Date: _____

Fiction Writing Frames for Infants

Little Jack Horner

Little _____

Sat _____

Eating _____

He _____

And _____

And said _____

_____

Name: _____ Date: _____

Jack and Jill

Jack _____

To _____

Jack _____

And _____

And Jill _____

Up _____

As _____

He _____

And _____

In _____

Helpful Words

pail	fetch	broke	vinegar
crown	tumbling	wrapped	

Name: _____ Date: _____

Little Miss Muffet

Little _____

Sat _____

Eating _____

Along _____

And _____

And _____

Helpful Words

tuffet   curds   whey   spider
frightened

Name: _____ Date: _____

Fiction Writing Frames for Infants

Old Mother Hubbard

Old _____

Went _____

To _____

But _____

The _____

And so _____

Helpful Words

cupboard   bone   bare   none

Use this writing frame to write another
nursery rhyme with two different characters.

Name: _____   Date: _____

My Favourite Nursery Rhyme

My favourite nursery rhyme is _____

_____

I like this rhyme because _____

_____

_____

_____

_____

The funniest part is when _____

_____

_____

_____

_____

My favourite character is _____

_____

because _____

_____

_____

Name: _____ Date: _____

Fiction Writing Frames for Infants © Belair (copiable page)

Jack and the Beanstalk

The story begins in _____

Jack's mother asks Jack _____

_____

_____

Jack swaps _____

_____

_____

The beanstalk _____

_____

_____

The words the giant says many times are

Name: _____ Date: _____

Fiction Writing Frames for Infants

Little Red Riding Hood

Read the words of Little Red Riding Hood and write in the wolf's reply.

"Grandma, what big eyes you've got."

"All _____

_____. "

"Grandma, what big ears you've got."

"All _____

_____. "

"Grandma, what a big nose you've got."

"All _____

_____. "

"Grandma, what big teeth you've got."

"All _____

_____. "

Name: _____   Date: _____

Fiction Writing Frames for Infants   © Belair (copiable page)

The Three Little Pigs

Read the story of The Three Little Pigs.

The first little pig built _____

_____

The second little _____

_____

The third _____

_____

When the wolf stood outside each house, he said,

" _____

_____

_____

_____ "

The pigs' reply was always, " _____

_____

_____

_____ "

Name: _____ Date: _____

My Favourite Fairy Tale

My favourite fairy tale is _____

_____

I like it because _____

_____

_____

_____

My favourite character is _____

_____

because _____

_____

_____

_____

If I could change the ending, I would _____

_____

_____

_____

_____

Name: _____   Date: _____

Fairy Tale Characters

Fairy tales usually have good and bad characters. Complete the chart and write a sentence about each character.

Fairy Tale	Characters
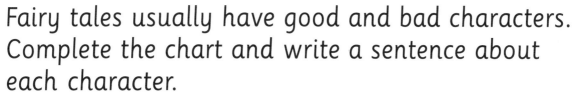 Sleeping Beauty	Good: Bad:
Snow White and the Seven Dwarfs	Good: Bad:
Rumplestiltskin	Good: Bad:
Jack and the Beanstalk	Good: Bad:

Name: _____ Date: _____

Fiction Writing Frames for Infants

Fairy Tale Beginnings

Fairy tales can begin in lots of different ways. Think of a story you know and write three different beginnings.

Helpful Story Beginnings

Once upon a time ...

There once was ...

Many, many years ago ...

Long, long ago ...

Name: _____   Date: _____

Fiction Writing Frames for Infants © Belair (copiable page)

A Fairy Tale I Know

A fairy tale I know is _____

_____

Once upon a time, _____

_____

_____

_____

Sadly, _____

_____

_____

Happily, _____

_____

_____

Finally, _____

_____

_____

_____

Name: _____ Date: _____

My Own Fairy Tale

The title of my own fairy tale is _____

_____

There are _____ characters.

● _____ is a _____

who _____

● _____ is a _____

who _____

● _____ is a _____

who _____

The main plot of the story is _____

_____

_____

_____

_____

At the end, _____

_____

_____

Name: _____ Date: _____

Counting Rhymes I

One, two, three, four, five

_____

_____

Six, seven, eight, nine, ten

_____

_____

Why _____

_____

Because _____

_____

Which _____

_____

This _____

Name: _____ Date: _____

Counting Rhymes II

One, two _____

_____

Three, four _____

_____

Five, six _____

_____

Seven, eight _____

_____

Nine, ten _____

_____

Helpful Words

shoe	sticks	hen	new	bricks
pen	door	gate	more	late

Name: _____   Date: _____

Primary Fiction Writing Frames for Infants   © Belair (copiable page)

Late for School

Seven in the morning

It's time to stop _____

I'm in a rush

My teeth need a _____

It feels like a race

I must wash _____

Just past the hour

No time for a _____

I'm sure to be late

Better race through the _____

My mum forgot to say,

"Don't you know it's Saturday!"

Name: _____   Date: _____

Primary Fiction Writing Frames for Infants

Parts of Me

Two eyes that I can see with

Two _____

One _____

One _____

One _____

Ten _____

Two _____

Two _____

Two _____

And it all adds up to ME.

Name: _____   Date: _____

Opposites

Up, down

Wear a _____

Left, right

Out of _____

In, out

Fall _____

Under, over

I'm in _____

Flip, flop

Time to _____

Name: _____ Date: _____

Fiction Writing Frames for Infants

Look What I Can Do

Clop, clop

I can _____

Clip, clip

I can _____

Beep, beep

I _____

Hoot, hoot

_____

Tap, tap

_____

Name: _____ Date: _____

Fiction Writing Frames for Infants

A Story from Africa

The best African story I know is _____

_____

The story is about _____

_____

_____

_____

What I really like in the story is when _____

_____

_____

I know it is an African story because _____

_____

_____

_____

_____

Name: _____ Date: _____

An Indian Story

My favourite story from India is _____

_____

_____

It takes place in _____

_____

_____

I can tell it is an Indian story by _____

_____

_____

The main characters are _____

_____

_____

The story makes me feel _____

because _____

_____

_____

Name: _____ Date: _____

Stories About Distant Places

A story I know about a far-away place is _____

_____

The place is _____

_____

The main character is called _____

The story is about _____

_____

_____

_____

_____

The place is different to where I live because

_____

_____

_____

_____

_____

Name: _____ Date: _____

Fiction Writing Frames for Infants

Missing Person
Pinocchio

Pinocchio does not look like other boys because

_____

_____

Pinocchio tells lies.
When he does _____

_____

_____

_____

Pinocchio was last seen _____

_____

If you see him, please _____

_____

Name: _____ Date: _____

Fiction Writing Frames for Infants

The Tortoise and the Hare

One day the hare said to _____

" _____

_____

_____. "

And the moral of the story is _____

_____

Name: _____   Date: _____

Fiction Writing Frames for Infants

My Favourite Character

My favourite character is _____.

_____ is a character in

_____

_____ is my favourite character

because _____

_____

_____

and _____

_____

The thing I do not like about _____

is _____

_____

If I could change _____

_____

I would _____

_____

Name: _____   Date: _____

Fiction Writing Frames for Infants   © Belair (copiable page)

Character Behaviour

The story I have chosen is _____

_____

The character, I will write about is _____

_____ , who acted like _____

_____

_____

I think that this behaviour was _____

because _____

_____

_____

_____

Another character who behaved like this was

_____ in the story of _____

_____

_____

_____

Name: _____ Date: _____

Fiction Writing Frames for Infants

Character Appearance

The character I have chosen is _____ .

_____ is about _____ tall

and weighs _____ .

_____ 's face is _____ with

_____ hair, _____ eyes, a

_____ mouth, _____ ears

and a _____ nose.

_____ usually wears _____

_____

and _____ on his/her feet

Sketch of

_____

Name: _____ Date: _____

Fiction Writing Frames for Infants © Belair (copiable page)

Wanted

Name _____

Appearance _____

_____

_____

_____

Last seen _____

_____

_____

Reason _____

_____

_____

Reward _____

_____

Name: _____ Date: _____

Bigger and Bigger

One day the farmer planted _____

It grew _____ and _____

until _____

So the farmer _____

_____

But _____

_____

_____

Then _____

_____

_____

But still _____

_____

_____

In the end, _____

_____

_____

Name: _____ Date: _____

Fiction Writing Frames for Infants

Tongue Twisters

Some words are difficult to say together.
Say these words as fast as you can.

She sells sea shells on the sea shore.

Choose words which begin with the same letter
to write tongue twisters.

Tim told _____

Mary makes _____

Sam said _____

Nutty Nora _____

Rani rarely _____

Fred fears _____

Now ask a friend to read them fast.
Are they good tongue twisters?

Name: _____ Date: _____

Riddles

What bird can fly but cannot cheep?

Answer: A ladybird

Think of riddle questions for these answers.

_____

_____

Answer: Seahorse

_____

_____

Answer: Daisychain

_____

_____

Answer: Lifebelt

_____

_____

Answer: Doorbell

Name: _____ Date: _____

Fiction Writing Frames for Infants

© Belair (copiable page)

My Favourite Poet

My favourite poet is _____

Poems I know are

_____

_____

My favourite poem is

_____

because _____

_____

_____

_____

A question I would like to ask my favourite poet is

_____

_____

_____

_____

Name: _____   Date: _____

Fiction Writing Frames for Infants

My Favourite Author

My favourite author is _____

_____

Books I know are _____

_____

_____

_____

What I like about the stories is _____

_____

_____

_____

If I met the author, a question I would ask is

_____

_____

_____

_____

Name: _____ Date: _____